555
Sticker Fun
Fairies

Sandy Creek
NEW YORK

An Imprint of Sterling Publishing
387 Park Avenue South
New York, NY 10016

SANDY CREEK and the distinctive Sandy Creek logo are registered trademarks of Barnes & Noble, Inc.
Text © 2014 Tide Mill Media. Illustrations © 2014 Tide Mill Media
This 2014 edition published by Sandy Creek.

ISBN 978-1-4351-5458-2
Manufactured in China
Lot #:
2 4 6 8 10 9 7 5 3 1
03/14

Spring cleaning

Spring has arrived in the magical woods. It is time for the fairies to spring-clean their treehouses. Fill the scene with fairies sweeping, washing and polishing until everything gleams.

Fancy fairy cakes

Today, it is very busy in the fairies' kitchen. Use stickers to fill it with fairies baking and decorating special fairy cakes for the Fairy Queen.

The perfect treehouse

The fairies are spending the evening designing the perfect treehouse. Use the fairy stickers to show them bringing their ideas to life on the paper.

Spell time!

Once a week, the fairies go to spell practice at the palace. Fill the room with wand-waving fairies making showers of twinkling stars appear out of thin air.

Rainy day

It is a very rainy day indeed. The fairies must be careful not to get their delicate wings wet. Complete the scene with fairies hiding under the leaves until the rain stops.

Fairground fun

As a special treat, the fairies are enjoying a day at the fairground.
Use the stickers to find them all a seat on the magical carousel.
What fun!

Dragon danger!

The dragon has fallen asleep in the palace garden! Fill the scene with fairies tying him down with magical ribbons, in case he wakes up and causes mayhem. Be very quiet!

Busy tooth fairies

It is Christmas time and the tooth fairies are extra busy.
They must deliver gold coins to all of the children who have lost
a tooth. Use stickers to complete the snowy rooftop scene.

The Starlight Dance Troupe

The fairy ballerinas are going to perform for the Fairy Queen.
Fill the stage with dancing fairies, twirling around and around
in their pretty tutus.

Wicked witch alert!

Uh-oh! The wicked witch is flying tonight! Complete the scene with nervous fairies peering out from the palace windows, hoping she does not spot them.

The Forest of Candy Delights

The fairies love visiting their friends in a nearby forest because the trees have candies as well as leaves! Fill the scene with fluttering fairies filling their baskets with sugary treats.

The Fairy Queen's bedroom

The Fairy Queen is in bed and it's her birthday today! Fill her bedroom with fairy visitors carrying flowers and gifts for her special day.

Beautiful quilt

The fairy sewing group is making a big patchwork quilt. Use stickers to complete the scene with fairies decorating one square each.

Hide-and-go-seek

The palace garden is a good place for playing hide-and-go-seek.
The fairies wear dresses that match the plants to make hiding easier.
Stick each fairy in a place where she is hard to spot.

Fairy lights

The fairies decorate the palace to make a pretty nighttime scene. Add fairies putting up fairy lights to make the palace twinkle in the darkness.

Tea party

It is time for afternoon tea with sandwiches, buns and a big cake.
Surround the table with fairies enjoying the delicious food. Yummy!

Secret wishes

Once in a while, the fairies grant some secret wishes—but only for good children. Show them flying high above the village to find the houses they must visit.

Flower fairies

The palace garden needs love and attention to keep it looking pretty.
Fill the scene with fairies digging, weeding and picking flowers for
the Fairy Queen.

Four-legged friends

The unicorns are waiting to be fed and groomed. Fill the scene with fairies taking care of their special four-legged friends.

Special potion

The fairies want to create a secret potion with a lovely smell and special powers. Fill the scene with fairies mixing, pouring, sniffing and tasting, doing their best to get the recipe right.

The butterfly race

It is the day of the big butterfly race. The palace is buzzing with excitement! Fill the sky with fairies riding butterflies, racing toward the finish line. Who will win this year?

Midsummer magic

It is midsummer's night and the unicorns are prancing in a moonlit glade. Add the unicorns then fill the treetops with fluttering fairies, watching the magical scene below.

The Fairy Queen's ball

Every year, the Fairy Queen holds a ball with a banquet and dancing.
Fill the ballroom with happy fairies in beautiful ball gowns and
sparkling tiaras.

Sweet dreams

It is getting late so the fairies must go to bed. Complete the scene with fairies in front of their treehouses, waving goodnight to their friends.